# EMELI SANDÉ

## OUR VERSION OF EVENTS

Published by
**Hal Leonard Europe**
A Music Sales / Hal Leonard Joint Venture Company
14-15 Berners Street, London W1T 3LJ, UK.

Order No. HLE90004497
ISBN 978-1-78038-652-2
This book © Copyright 2012 Hal Leonard Corporation.

Music edited by Jenni Norey.
Music arranged by Derek Jones.
Music processed by Paul Ewers Music Design.
Printed in the EU.

# EMELI SANDÉ

## OUR VERSION OF EVENTS

Exclusively distributed by

**HAL LEONARD EUROPE**

# HEAVEN

WORDS & MUSIC BY EMELI SANDÉ, MIKE SPENCER,
HARRY CRAZE, SHAHID KHAN & HUGO CHEGWIN

1. Will you re-cog-nise me in the flash-ing lights?____
2. Will you re-cog-nise me when I'm steal-ing from the poor?__

# WHERE I SLEEP

WORDS & MUSIC BY SHAHID KHAN & EMELI SANDÉ

this is us, this is love_____ and this is where___ I sleep.___

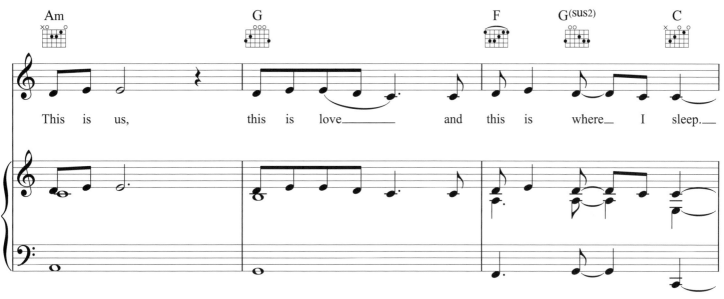

This is us, this is love_____ and this is where___ I sleep.___

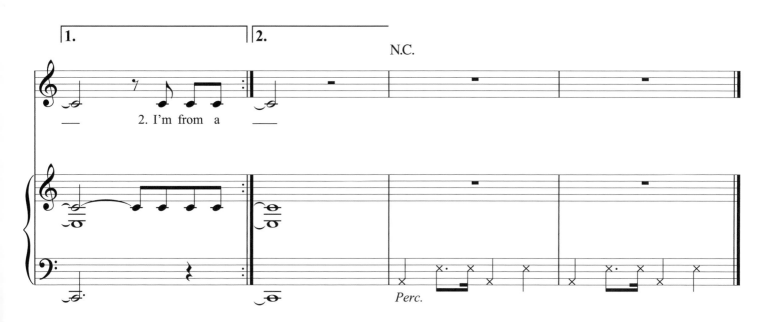

**1.**    **2.**    N.C.

2. I'm from a

Perc.

# MY KIND OF LOVE

## WORDS & MUSIC BY EMILE HAYNIE, EMELI SANDÉ & DANIEL TANNENBAUM

It beats on-ly for you. 'Cause when you've

giv-en up,___ when no mat-ter what___ you do___ it's nev-er

good e-nough,___ when you nev-er thought___ that it could ev-er

get this tough,_____ that's when you feel my kind___ of___ love.___

18

# MOUNTAINS

WORDS & MUSIC BY MUSTAFA OMER, SHAHID KHAN,
EMELI SANDÉ, JAMES MURRAY & LUKE JUBY

Yeah,_____ we'll climb moun - tains, climb moun - tains to - geth-
*2° Instrumental ad lib.*

- er. Yeah,_____ we'll climb moun - tains, climb moun - tains to - geth -

- er.

# CLOWN

WORDS & MUSIC BY SHAHID KHAN, EMELI SANDÉ
& GRANT MITCHELL

# DADDY

WORDS & MUSIC BY JAMES MURRAY, MUSTAFA OMER,
SHAHID KHAN, EMELI SANDÉ & GRANT MITCHELL

# MAYBE

## WORDS & MUSIC BY PAUL HERMAN, EMELI SANDÉ & ASHTON MILLARD

1. When we first moved in together couldn't keep hands off each oth-
2. We broke up last Sunday night keep on thinking 'bout the fight.

But I don't wan-na give up what we've got.
But I don't wan-na give up yet be-cause…

May-be you could stay_ a bit long-er, I could try_ a bit hard-er. We could make_ this

work. But may-be we should stop_ pre-tend-ing. We both know_ we're
Both of us_ are

hurt-ing. May-be it's time_ to go. go.

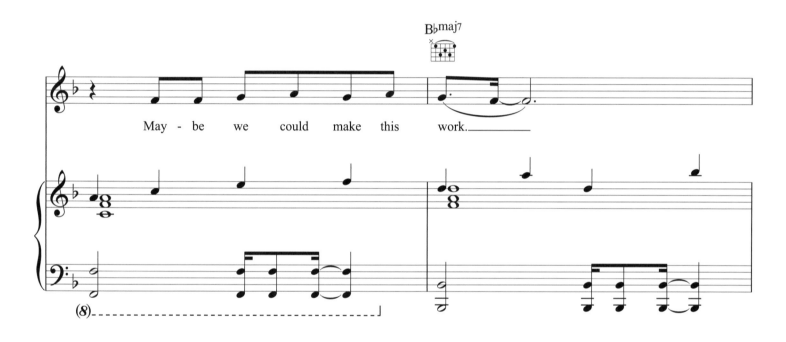

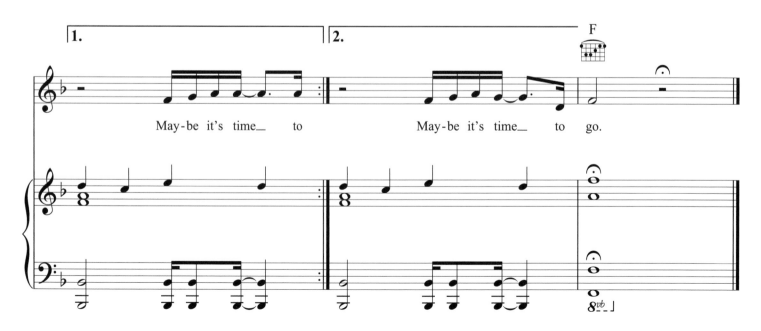

40

# RIVER

WORDS & MUSIC BY SHAHID KHAN & EMELI SANDÉ

1. If you're

look-ing for the big ad-ven-ture and gold is all that's on your
(2.) want are ans-wers to your ques-tions and you can't seem to find no love for

43

44

Wher - ev - er you're stand - ing     I will be___ by    your   side.___

Through the    good,         through the bad,___    I'll

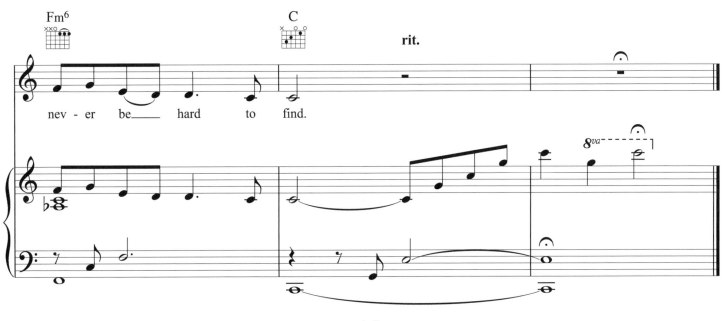

nev - er   be___ hard   to   find.

rit.

# SUITCASE

WORDS & MUSIC BY SHAHID KHAN, EMELI SANDÉ
& BENJAMIN HARRISON

1. Did-n't see it com - ing, no kind of warn - ing.
2. What changed so quick - ly? An - swer me! If you

I can't work out what I've done wrong.
must kill me at least please tell me why.

His clothes are miss - ing but his key's still here.
He says "don't touch me, get out the way." Will

Please some-bod - y tell me what's go - ing on.
some - one tell me what's go - ing on to - night?
My ba - by's got a

suit - case. He's tell - ing me it's too late. But

don't no - bod - y, please don't ask me why. 'Cause all I did was

48

heart 'cause he won't look at me an-y-more._____ My ba-by's got a

# BREAKING THE LAW

WORDS & MUSIC BY SHAHID KHAN, EMELI SANDÉ
& BENJAMIN HARRISON

# NEXT TO ME

WORDS & MUSIC BY HARRY CRAZE, HUGO CHEGWIN,
EMELI SANDÉ & ANUK PAUL

1. You won't find__ him drink - ing un - der ta - bles,
2. You won't find__ him try'n' to change__ the dev - il

roll - ing__ dice__ and stay - ing out__ till three.
for mon - ey, fame,__ for pow - er, out__ of greed.

# LIFETIME

WORDS & MUSIC BY SHAHID KHAN, EMELI SANDÉ,
LUKE JUBY, STEVE MOSTYN & GLYN AIKINS

1. Dream-ing on - ly lasts un-til you

wake up and you find you're not a - sleep.

Si-lence on - ly sticks a-round till some-one in the room de-cides to speak.

# READ ALL ABOUT IT, PART III

### WORDS & MUSIC BY SHAHID KHAN & EMELI SANDÉ

1. You've got the

words to change a na-tion but you're bit-ing your tongue. You've spent a
(2.) wak-ing up the neigh-bours while we sing a-way the blues. Mak-ing

we're a lit-tle dif-f'rent. There's no need to be a-shamed. You've got the
time we got some air-play of our ver-sion of e-vents. There's no

light to fight the shad-ows, so stop hid-ing it a-way.___
need to be a-fraid, I will sing with you my friend.___

Come on, come on.___
Come on, come on.___

I wan-na sing,___

I wan-na shout.___ I wan-na scream___ till the words___ dry out.___

# TIGER

### WORDS & MUSIC BY SHAHID KHAN & EMELI SANDÉ

1. Drop all the pills doc-tor told us to take. They say we're dream-in' but I swear we're a-wake. When-

2. You'll build a plane and I'll build a boat. If we drop all the sil-ver I swear we can float. Was-n't

-ev-er you leave all the col-ours fade._ So I'm here hold-ing on 'cause I'm tired of grey._ Are you

born for the mon-ey so I spend it___ quick. Bank says I'm poor but I'm feel-in' rich._ If you're

# HOPE

WORDS & MUSIC BY ALICIA KEYS & EMELI SANDÉ